GW00385510

Published by **Redemptorist Publications**
A registered charity, limited by guarantee. Registered in England 3261721.

Original text by Yvonne Fordyce, copyright © Redemptorist Publications, 2007
Illustrations copyright © Finola Stack, 2007

This edition © Redemptorist Publications, 2007

ISBN 978-0-85231-344-2

All rights reserved. No part of this publication may be reproduced, stored in a retrieval system, or transmitted in any form or by any means, electronic, mechanical, photocopying, recording or otherwise, without prior permission in writing from Redemptorist Publications.

A catalogue record for this book is available from the British Library

The moral rights of the illustrator have been asserted.

Printed by Estudios Gráficos, Zure, Spain

Alphonsus House Chawton Hampshire GU34 3HQ
Telephone 01420 88222
Fax 01420 88805
rp@rpbooks.co.uk
www.rpbooks.co.uk

The Story of ESTHER

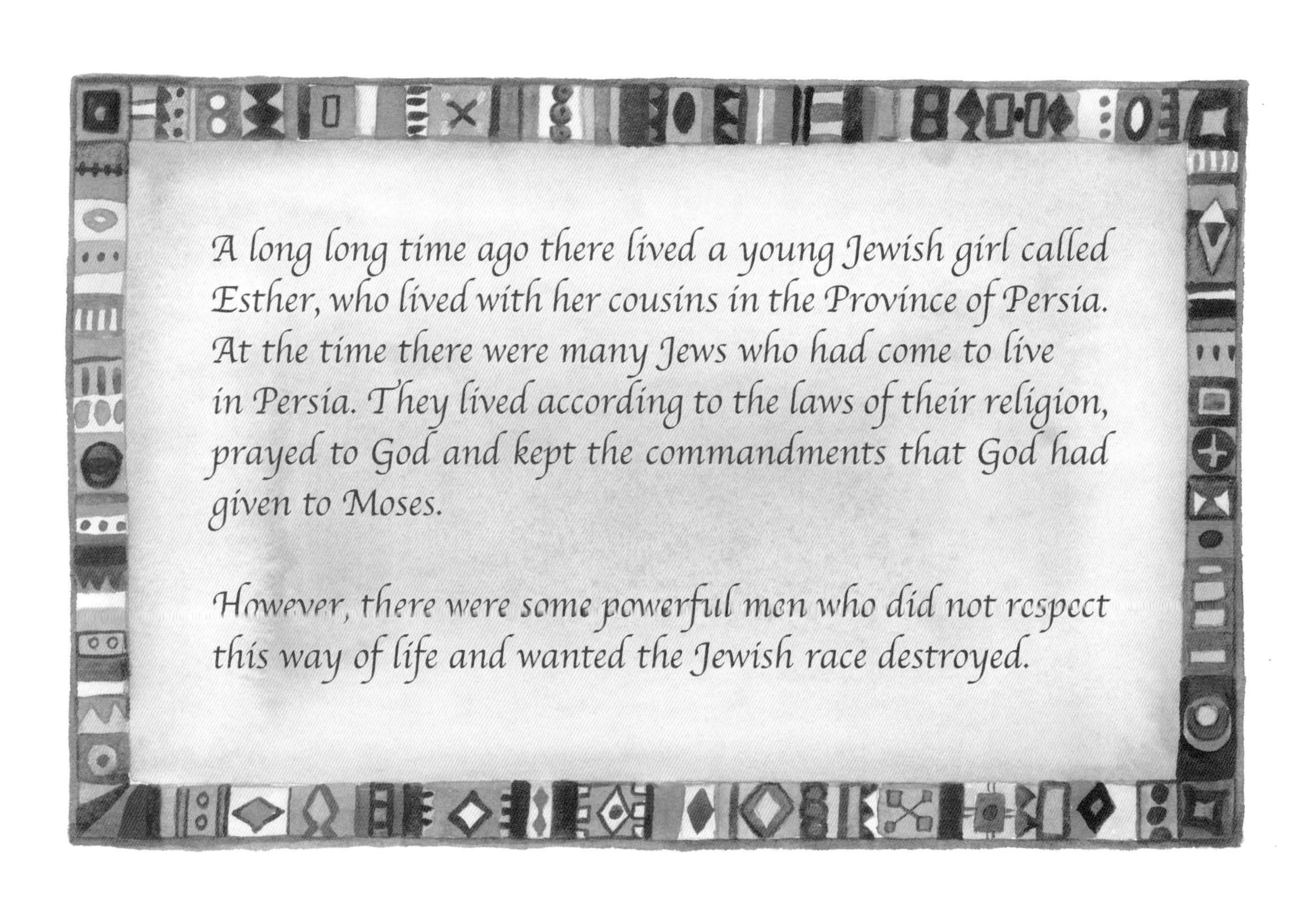

A long long time ago there lived a young Jewish girl called Esther, who lived with her cousins in the Province of Persia. At the time there were many Jews who had come to live in Persia. They lived according to the laws of their religion, prayed to God and kept the commandments that God had given to Moses.

However, there were some powerful men who did not respect this way of life and wanted the Jewish race destroyed.

This is the story of how Esther became queen, and how, later, she saved her people.

Esther's parents had died when she was young. Mordecai, her kind cousin, adopted her as his daughter and brought her to live with his family on their farmland.

They shared the work, their meals, the daily prayers, and the parties and celebrations of the Jewish household. Esther grew up to be a fine young woman whom everyone admired.

The Province of Persia, where Mordecai and Esther lived, was one of one hundred and twenty-seven provinces ruled over by King Xerxes.

His huge empire stretched from India to Ethiopia and was made up of a number of races with their different cultures and customs.

King Xerxes liked to show off his wealth and be known as a king who deserved admiration and respect. He once gave a banquet, at his splendid palace, that lasted one hundred and eighty days. All his ministers, army chiefs, noblemen and governors were present.

Nobody dared refuse an invitation to the king's palace:
King Xerxes' commands HAD to be obeyed.

When a guest entered the palace he would have been overwhelmed by the riches and beauty around him. Elegant gold and silver couches stood on a floor of marble and shining mother-of-pearl. White and violet wall hangings were fastened to silver rings on marble columns with cords of fine linen and purple thread. Wine was served in gold cups of varied and extravagant design.

The time came when the king was ready to choose a queen. As was the custom, courtiers from the palace were sent to the one hundred and twenty-seven provinces in search of beautiful girls to bring to the harem, the rooms in the palace where the women lived.

Esther was one of those chosen, and her cousin Mordecai had encouraged her to seek a more comfortable life in the palace.

Before being presented to the king, all the women had to undergo a long period of beauty treatment in order to look stunningly beautiful in the presence of the king.

Esther was bathed in sweet perfume and spices. Her hair was braided with fine ribbon and beads and she was given elegant robes to wear.

All who knew her not only admired her for her beauty, but loved her for her good nature and happy disposition.

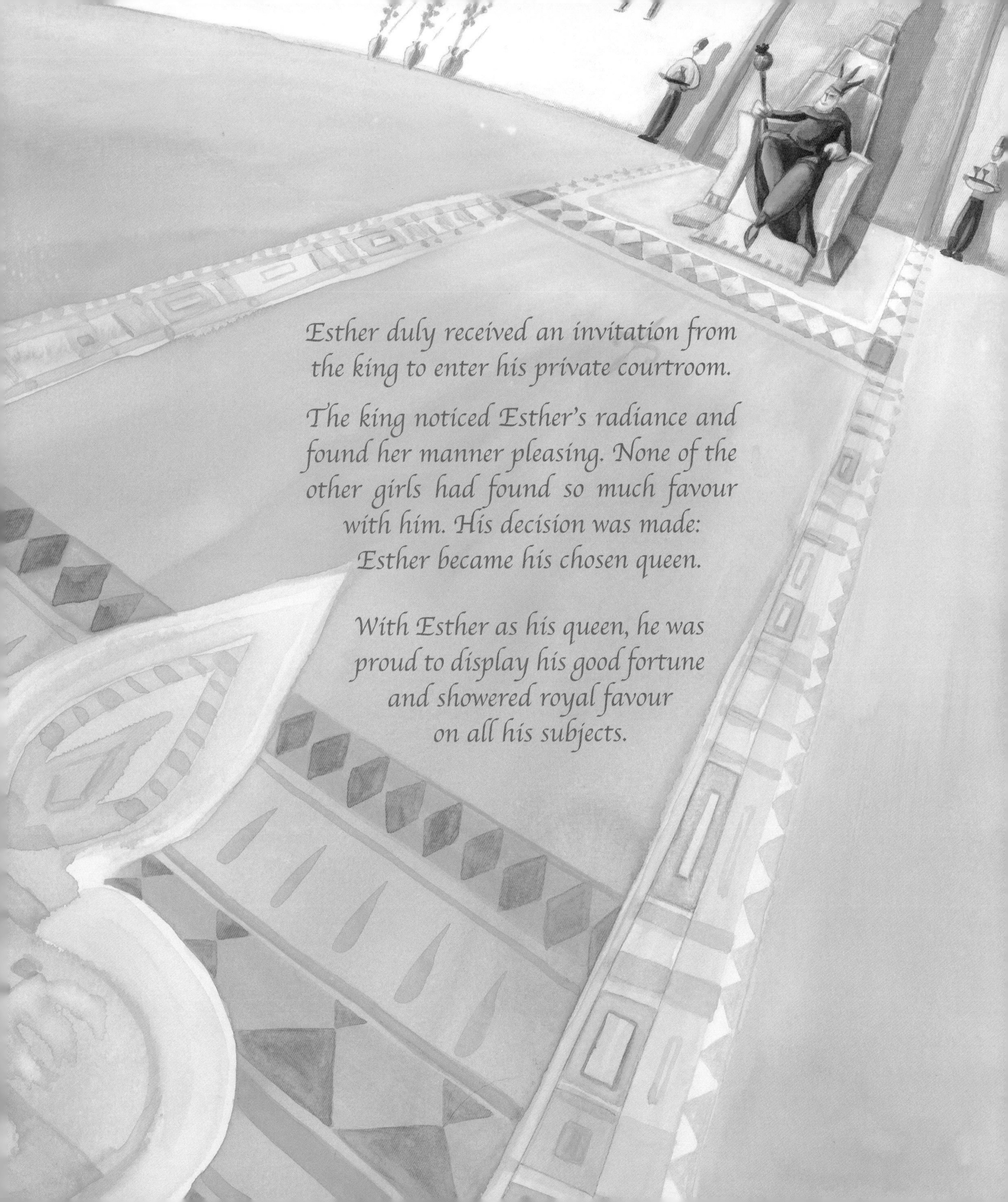

Esther duly received an invitation from the king to enter his private courtroom.

The king noticed Esther's radiance and found her manner pleasing. None of the other girls had found so much favour with him. His decision was made: Esther became his chosen queen.

With Esther as his queen, he was proud to display his good fortune and showered royal favour on all his subjects.

The king held a
celebration banquet
and declared a public
holiday for all the provinces.
The feast lasted seven days
and seven nights. The tables
draped in sumptuous fabrics
were laden with delectable food,
and wine flowed in abundance.

Within the palace there were many rooms and courtyards. According to custom the women lived in the harem. Esther passed the time happily with her female friends and kept in contact with Mordecai, who now worked at the palace, through letters delivered by her servants.

Only when the king invited her did she spend time with him in his private courtroom.

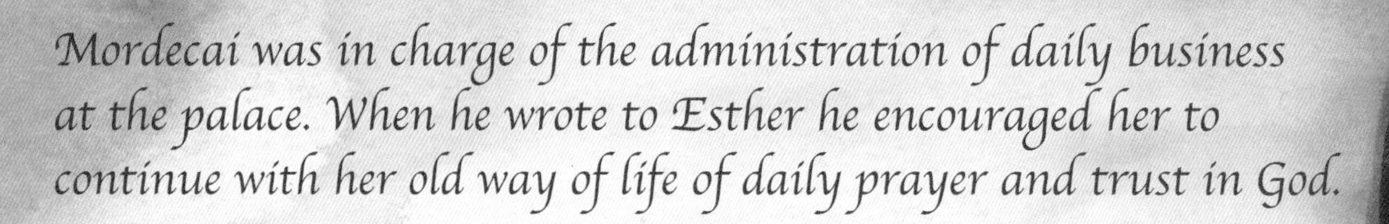

Mordecai was in charge of the administration of daily business at the palace. When he wrote to Esther he encouraged her to continue with her old way of life of daily prayer and trust in God.

Now, it was unknown to the king, and those in the palace, that Queen Esther and Mordecai were related. Consequently, nobody realised that Esther, too, was Jewish. Esther and Mordecai thought it best to keep their Jewish identity secret, as in these times Jews were often persecuted by the Persians.

One day, Mordecai was at the palace gates when he overheard two guards plotting to kill the king. They were jealous of the king's power and hoped to win favour with another king.

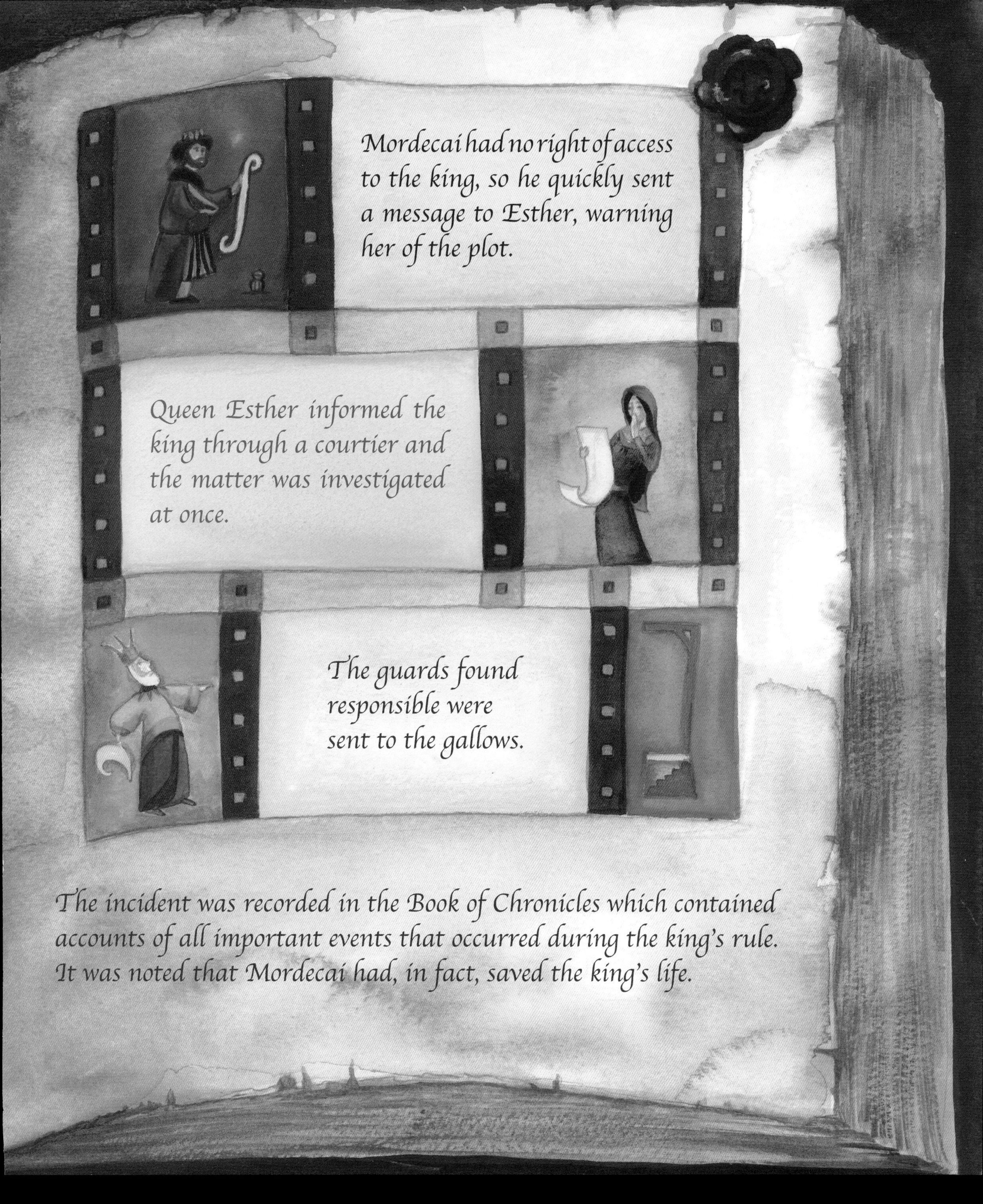

Mordecai had no right of access to the king, so he quickly sent a message to Esther, warning her of the plot.

Queen Esther informed the king through a courtier and the matter was investigated at once.

The guards found responsible were sent to the gallows.

The incident was recorded in the Book of Chronicles which contained accounts of all important events that occurred during the king's rule. It was noted that Mordecai had, in fact, saved the king's life.

Shortly afterwards, the king singled out, for promotion, a self-important man called Haman. He appointed him in charge of all the palace officials. Even the king's advisers and noblemen were under his command.

He was an arrogant man who sought glory and honour from those under his authority. Mordecai was one of his inferiors.

In order to recognise the importance of Haman's new position, the king gave orders that all those of lower rank were to bow down and prostrate themselves before Haman.

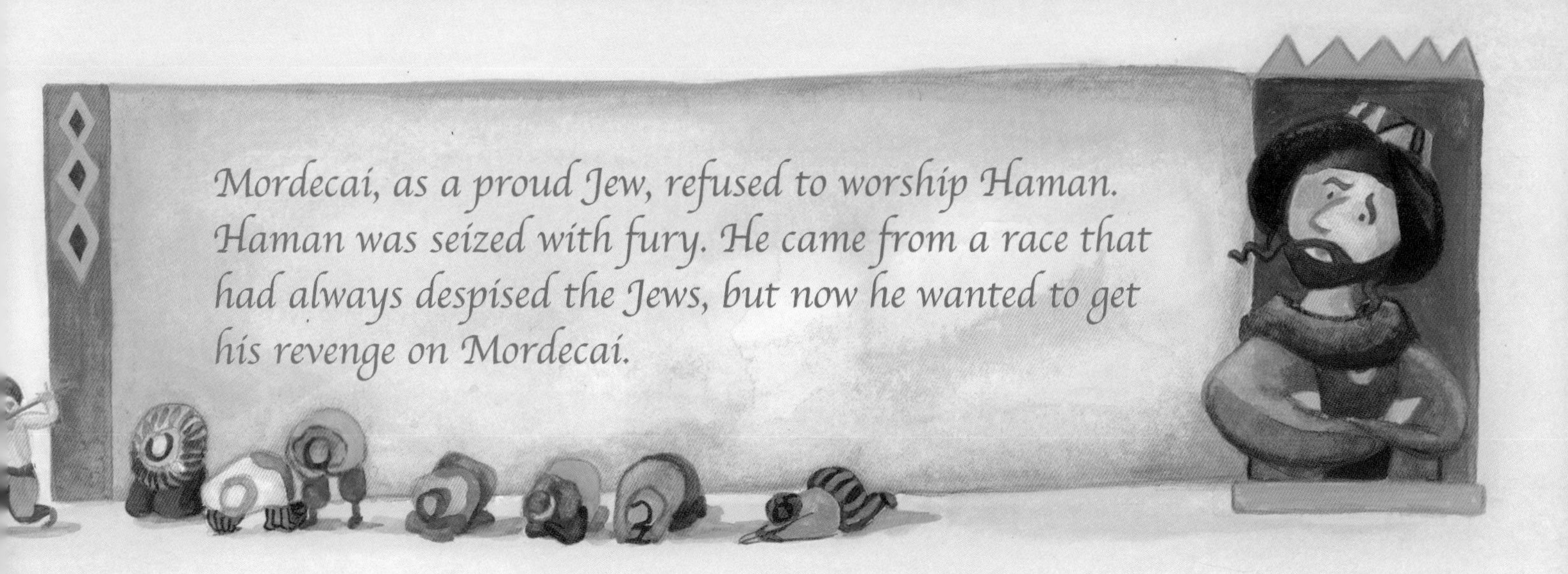

Mordecai, as a proud Jew, refused to worship Haman. Haman was seized with fury. He came from a race that had always despised the Jews, but now he wanted to get his revenge on Mordecai.

Haman devised a cunning plan and, as the king's chief adviser, he met with the king.
"There are people who refuse to obey your laws," he said, "and they should not be tolerated." The king granted Haman the authority to punish this certain group however he thought necessary. The king had no wish to show mercy to disobedient servants.

The king had given his signet ring to Haman, so that the orders could be stamped with the royal seal, to show that he had authorised the action. The king trusted Haman and had no idea how evil were his intentions: to order the annihilation of all the Jews. Haman was full of high spirits that day – how well his plan was working!

But when Haman passed Mordecai at the palace gate, Mordecai neither stood up nor even stirred at his approach. Haman felt a wave of anger.
That evening he set out to construct a gallows fifty cubits high (seventy-five feet) on which to hang Mordecai the Jew, whom he despised.

When Mordecai heard news of the orders to destroy the Jewish race he cried aloud, with bitter tears. Mordecai sent messages to Queen Esther, imploring her to speak to the king.

"Do not imagine that you are safer than any other Jew just because you are in the royal palace. Who knows? Perhaps you have come to the throne for just such a time as this."

He and his fellow Jews began to pray to God in earnest, expressing sorrow for all their wrongdoings in the past and appealing to God to save them.

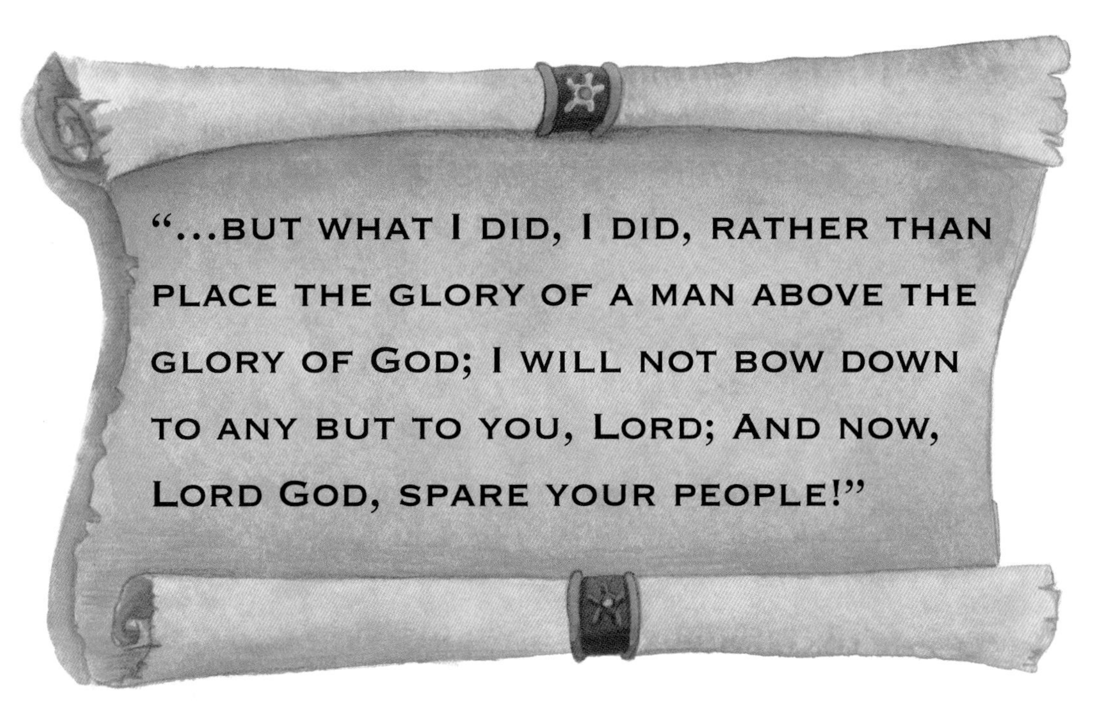

Esther knew that to approach the king in his inner court, without first being invited, was an action punishable by death. She was terrified.

She sent message to all her Jewish friends outside the palace to pray continually to God for her safety.

"As for me, give me courage, King of Gods and master of all power; Put persuasive words into my mouth when I face the lion; O God, listen to the voice of the desperate; save us from the hand of the wicked and free me from my fear."

Esther dressed herself in her finest robes. Her face radiated joy and love, but her heart shrank with fear. She arrived at the king's inner court. He was seated on the royal throne, dressed in all the robes of state, glittering with gold and precious stones: a formidable sight. Raising his face, he looked on her, blazing with anger.

Esther sank down, feeling faint and weak. But God changed the king's heart, inducing a milder spirit. He sprang from his throne in consternation and comforted her with soothing words, asking her the purpose of her visit. She was, indeed, one of his most treasured possessions.

Esther humbly invited the king and his chief adviser, Haman, to come to her banquet the following day.

Somehow that night the king found that he could not sleep.

He asked for the Book of Chronicles to be read out to him so that he could reflect on the achievements of his reign.

He listened to the record of the plot to kill him by two of his guards. It came to his notice that nothing had been done to reward Mordecai for saving his life.

Early the next morning while the king was still lying awake, contemplating how to reward such a noble action, Haman entered the king's chambers. He had come to seek the king's consent for Mordecai's death.

"Ah, my chief adviser," said the king, "you are the very person who could help me. What should be done for a man whom I want to honour greatly, for he deserves recognition from the king?"

Haman immediately assumed that he, himself, was the man who the king was pleased with, since he could think of no one else the king would want to honour.

So, greedily, he thought of all the aspects of the king's wealth and power that he desired for himself, and with sheer delight, he offered his advice to the king.

Haman replied:
"For the man the king wishes to honour, have him clothed in royal robes and bring him the king's horse with the royal crest on its head... Let one of the king's noble princes lead him through the streets proclaiming his greatness... Give him of your riches anything he desires."

"Hurry," said the king to Haman, "take the robes and the horse, and do everything you have just said, to Mordecai the Jew, who works at the palace gate. On no account leave anything out that you have mentioned."

Although Haman was overcome with shame and jealousy, he had to lead Mordecai on horseback through the city square proclaiming:

"This is the way to treat a man whom the king wishes to honour."

Even though Haman's scheme to kill Mordecai had failed, his orders to destroy the Jewish race were still in force. Queen Esther was worried for her people and had put her life in danger to approach the king uninvited.

The king asked Esther what it was she wanted from him. "If I have found favour in your eyes, O king," Queen Esther said, "and if it pleases your majesty, grant me my life and the lives of my people; for we are doomed to destruction and slaughter. The king will be dishonoured and lose many loyal subjects."

King Xerxes leapt up in rage.

"Where is this man, the schemer of such outrage?"

"Why, this wretch, Haman, is our persecutor!" Esther replied.

The king was enraged at Haman's wickedness when it was revealed that his Queen and also Mordecai, his trusted courtier, were both victims of the enforcement.

King Xerxes commanded Haman's orders to be cancelled and issued new ones enabling the Jewish race to be freed from their oppressors. The Jews were filled with relief and joy at the news.

As for Haman, he was hung on the very gallows that he had constructed for Mordecai. His land and possessions were given to Queen Esther and Mordecai became the king's much valued chief adviser.

The Jewish people today still celebrate Esther's courage.